Harry the Humorous Hippo

by

Zita Newcome

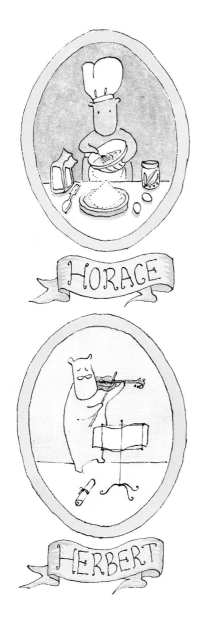

HORACE

HERBERT

HUMPHREY

HARRY

© THE MEDICI SOCIETY LTD · LONDON · 1987. Printed in England. B93 ISBN 0 85503 093 3

Harry the Hippo was feeling rather bored. He'd been round to his brothers' houses but none of them wanted to play with him. Horace was tidying up as usual, Herbert was practising on his violin and Humphrey was having an afternoon sleep.

'Miserable lot,' thought Harry.

In fact, Harry got bored rather easily, that's why he was always playing tricks on people and doing silly things.

'I wonder what I can do to make life more exciting round here,' he thought.

He was trying to think of something when his friend Bertie the bird landed on the window ledge.

'Hello Harry,' said Bertie, 'you look rather bored.'

'I am,' said Harry, 'my brothers won't play with me.'

'Well, can't you do something on your own?' asked Bertie. Harry thought this was rather a poor idea. 'I'm best at doing tricks and things, Bertie,' he said, 'and for that I need an audience.' Bertie had seen Harry do his conjuring acts before and knew this was true. 'Well, why don't you put on a show for them?' he said. Harry thought this was a better idea, but then they'd seen all his tricks before. 'Only Humphrey would enjoy them because he always forgets so quickly.' 'Well,' said Bertie, 'there's a new joke shop in town, why not get some new tricks?' 'What?' said Harry, 'A new joke shop?' Suddenly he was very excited. 'Well, what are we waiting for?'

And stopping just long enough to pick up some money he rushed off into town.

The joke shop was full of the most amazing tricks. 'Look at this,' shouted Harry. He had found a hat that could make an entire hippo disappear. He climbed into it and disappeared – only to reappear in another part of the shop.

'And this,' said Bertie. He was standing on a piece of glass that made him look twice as big as he really was. But that still wasn't very big! They rummaged around for nearly an hour before finally Harry had decided how much he could afford. He brought everything to the counter.

'I'll have all these tricks please,' he said, grinning with pleasure. But just then he spotted a large poster on the wall. It had a picture of the Royal Hippos and said:

THE HIGH HIPPO AND HER HIPPONESS
TO VISIT HIPPOVILLE ON 6th JULY

'That's in a few days,' said Bertie. Harry stared at it for a few seconds and then his eyes lit up.

'I've got a brilliant idea,' he said. 'I'm going to pretend to my brothers that I am the High Hippo!'

CIRCUS

'How?' asked Bertie. 'Well,' said Harry, 'the clothes he is wearing in the poster are just like the ones I've got in my dressing-up box. I'll get dressed up and when the High Hippo comes to town I'll pretend he's also visiting each of us but instead it'll be me!' He spluttered with laughter, 'It'll be such a laugh to see their faces as I inspect their homes.' 'But will they believe you?' asked Bertie. 'If I show them a poster, yes,' said Harry, 'Come on'.

He bought one of the posters, picked up his tricks and rushed off to find his brothers. 'Humphrey!' he shouted, 'Wake up and follow me, Herbert, stop playing that infernal instrument and come over here!' They followed him to Horace's house where Harry made them all sit down. He opened out the poster. 'Good news, Brothers,' he said. 'The High Hippo is coming to visit Hippoville and he wants to see us in our houses... PERSONALLY!' After some discussion the other hippos were soon in a state of great excitement. 'What do we do?' asked Humphrey.

'First thing', said Horace, 'we paint our houses.'

And so the preparation began.

They worked frantically but Horace had a hard time making sure things went smoothly: Herbert kept painting pretty patterns everywhere, Harry kept playing games like painting in false windows, and Humphrey kept forgetting where he'd painted and so more than once he painted the same place twice – and more than once he fell asleep while doing it. 'Next thing is to tidy the houses and then prepare some food for the High Hippo,' said Horace when all the houses were painted.

And so preparations went on until the very day of the visit. Horace had a quick look round all the houses. 'Good,' he said, 'I think we can be proud of ourselves. Let's go into town to see the Royal Hippos arrive.' At this point Harry couldn't help sniggering. 'What's up?' asked Horace. 'Nothing,' said Harry, 'It's just that I'm really looking forward to all this.'

And so they set off into town to see the procession.

The Royal Hippos rode slowly through the town and wherever they went there were hundreds of smiling, cheering hippos to greet them. 'How wonderful,' said Herbert, 'and to think that they want to see us!' 'Only the High Hippo,' said Harry, 'I gather Her Hipponess will rest while he travels out of town.' 'WHAT an honour,' said Horace. 'What's he called again?' asked Humphrey. The others laughed. 'We must go soon to get everything ready,' said Horace. The others agreed, so the hippos went off back to their homes.

But when the Royal Hippos came to an end of their tour and had a chance to sit down in private, although Her Hipponess was rather tired and hot and wanted a rest, the High Hippo was still keen to see more.

'I'd like to see some country Hippos,' he said to the Mayor. 'Oh dear,' replied the Mayor looking rather worried; he thought about it for a moment. 'The only ones I can think of nearby are four rather strange brothers who live beyond the watering hole.'

'Splendid!' shouted High Hippo, 'Ten minutes rest, then we'll sneak off to visit them – catch them unawares!' And he roared with laughter.

Leaving Her Hipponess to rest the High Hippo slipped out of the back door to avoid the crowds and set off to where the brothers lived. 'Are you sure this is a good plan?' asked the Mayor, 'after all, they *are* rather unusual hippos and they won't be expecting you.' 'Excellent!' said the High Hippo. 'I *never* get to meet unusual hippos', and he rushed on ahead.

The first house they came to was Horace's. 'What a splendid house – and how well looked after!' said High Hippo. At that point Horace appeared. 'Oh, Your Hipponess,' he began saying, 'I am honoured…' 'Oh forget all that business,' interrupted the High Hippo. 'Let's have a look inside'. Inside everything was gleaming and on the kitchen table was a great spread of food. 'It just so happened I was doing some cooking,' said Horace. 'Would you like some tea?' 'MARVELLOUS' exclaimed High Hippo, 'NUT PIE – my favourite.' He then tucked into a big tea and not until all the pie was finished did he stand up.

'Right,' he said, 'Let's go and see these other brothers of yours.'

The next house they came to was Herbert's. Just before they arrived the High Hippo stopped. 'What's that?' he asked. 'Herbert's playing the violin,' said Horace. 'Good Heavens, he's playing the Royal March – my favourite tune,' said the High Hippo. Horace smiled. The High Hippo stood for a few seconds listening to the music before marching in. 'Oh Your Hipponess,' said Horace, 'I am honoured...' 'Oh forget about all that,' interrupted High Hippo, 'That was *marvellous* music – play me something else now.

So Horace played all the tunes he had been told were the High Hippo's favourites. High Hippo was very pleased. 'All my favourite tunes,' he said, 'Well done... and what a nice house as well – I *am* enjoying myself.' They chatted for a while before High Hippo stood up again.

'Right, who's next?' he asked.

'Humphrey,' said Horace.

'Good, Humphrey it is then.'

They were soon at Humphrey's house where the brothers had helped put up the Royal flag above the chimney pot.

'Good Hippo!' said the High Hippo, 'I like to see Patriotism... Now where is he? But the only sound coming from inside was one of snoring. 'Oh dear,' muttered Horace, 'I feared this might happen.' 'Well?' said the High Hippo. 'I think he's asleep, sir,' said Horace. But instead of looking angry High Hippo laughed. 'Very wise,' he said, 'very wise... always try to get an afternoon nap in myself.' Horace and Herbert could hardly believe it and were wondering what to do next when Humphrey suddenly appeared in the doorway looking rather sleepy.

'Mr Humphrey, I presume,' said the High Hippo. Humphrey suddenly realised what was happening. 'Oh Good Heavens,' he said, 'Her Hoppiness... I mean, His Happiness, Oh dear... I mean Hot Hippiness.' Horace and Herbert moaned, but the High Hippo roared and roared with laughter.' 'Marvellous!' he shouted, 'Marvellous! Right, on to the last house!' And they set off towards Harry.

'I hope Harry's not up to anything silly,' whispered Horace to Herbert as they approached his house. But of course Harry was the only one not expecting the High Hippo. In fact he was inside and had just finished dressing up as the High Hippo himself and was about to go out to play his trick on his brothers. 'I suppose he's inside,' said the High Hippo, 'I'll just go on in and introduce myself.' And so he marched straight in... and came face to face with what looked like himself in a doorway. 'Good Heavens!' he said, 'I've never seen a mirror that big before', and started adjusting his gown.

Harry stared back in horror. 'Oh no,' he was thinking 'It's the real High Hippo.' Then he realised the High Hippo thought he was a mirror – so tried to copy his movements. It worked for a few seconds but then Harry was shaking so much with fear that the crown fell off his head. The High Hippo stopped and stared at him.

'H..H.. how do you do, Your Hipponess,' squeaked Harry, 'I am H..Harry the Hippo!'

For a long moment there was absolute silence. The High Hippo stared at all the brothers who were looking terrified. 'What is the meaning of this?' he said fiercely. 'Well sir,' said Harry, 'It was going to be a practical joke on my brothers – I told them you would be visiting and then I dressed up to look like you…' There was another long silence. Then slowly the High Hippo began to smile. 'So that's why they were playing my favourite music, flying my flag, and cooking my favourite food.' And he began to laugh and laugh and laugh.

Before he left he issued them all with invitations to his castle. 'Haven't been so amused in years,' he said, 'Splendid! Splendid!' And as he was going, Bertie the bird came and landed on Harry's shoulder. 'Phew!' he said, 'Was that exciting enough?' But Harry was so speechless he could only nod.

CW01052164

THE CORNISH DI.
THE CORNISH LANGUAGE

Pol Hodge

Kesva an Taves Kernewek
The Cornish Language Board
© *1997*

ISBN 0 907064 58 2

Raglavar
Forward

The rapid expansion and enhanced status of the Cornish language has recently attracted much attention.

This short treatise aims to present an objective view of the Cornish dialect and in particular its overlap with *Kernewek,* the Cornish language. It also hopes to show the variations according to the different regions of Cornwall and the variation through time, quoting the dialect collectors of the 1880s as well as those of 1990s.

Often the word Cornish, as applied to speech, is confusing as some use it to define the dialect i.e. the distinct form of the English language spoken in Cornwall while others define Cornish as the Celtic language also spoken in Cornwall. So this booklet uses Cornish as anything related to the land of Cornwall and *Kernewek* as anything related to the Celtic language.

This booklet is based on the author's upbringing in Troon, a former mining village, two miles south of Camborne in West Cornwall. It is also based on the contact with various people encountered while learning and teaching Kernewek in London, Camborne, Liskeard, Pengegon, Grampound Road, St. Austell and Truro.

> Pol Hodge is secretary of **Kowethas an Yeth Kernewek** (The Cornish Language Fellowship). He is a teacher of Kernewek and an accomplished poet writing mainly in Kernewek. He lives in Grampound Road with his wife, Jane Ninnis, currently the Sales Officer for the Kowethas. He is also a member of **Kesva an Taves Kernewek** (The Cornish Language Board), a language bard of **Gorsedh Kernow** (The Cornish Gorsedd) and a simultaneous translator for **Iskessedhek Kernewek an Burow Europek rag Yethow Nebes Kewsys** (The Cornish sub-committee of the European Bureau of Lesser Used Languages).

THE CORNISH DIALECT AND THE CORNISH LANGUAGE

1. What is Dialect?

The Concise Oxford Dictionary states that dialect is a "form of speech peculiar to a district, class, or person, a subordinate variety of a language with a distinguishable vocabulary, pronunciation, or idioms."

2. What is Cornish Dialect?

In the following discussion the language is question is the English language and the 'subordinate variety' is the Cornish dialect. A second language has also had an influence on the Cornish dialect - Kernewek. The Cornish dialect is the form of the English language spoken in Cornwall. This simple definition needs clarification due to the fact that there are two dialects in Cornwall. As long ago as 1880 The English Dialect Society published 'Glossary of Words in Use in Cornwall.' This book was written in two parts; Miss M.A. Courtney wrote the first half which deals with the West Cornish Dialect and Thomas Q. Couch the dialect of East Cornwall (see map, below).

ENGLISH DIALECT SOCIETY.

This model was slightly modified by Martyn Wakelin in 'Language and History of Cornwall' when he found the two dialects had a transition zone around mid Cornwall. The situation becomes further complicated when the tin and copper mines of West Cornwall began to fail and miners moved 'up East' to work in the clay industry and the mines of Caradon and North Cornwall. Thomas Q. Couch in 1880 says,

> "These immigrants brought with them and have left an infusion of their language especially, the technical portion..."

With the mobility of increased car ownership and changing patterns of work, one could argue that these distinctions have been blurred to give us one Cornish dialect. The most obvious feature that sets Cornish dialect apart from Standard English is its vocabulary.

Cornish Dialect	Standard English
abroad	open
baissly	dirty
ugly	ill-tempered
bannel	the broom plant
clunk	to swallow
quilkin, whilkey	a frog

The first three are English words that have acquired different meanings. The second three examples are derived from Kernewek. There are hundreds of words in the Cornish dialect that come from Kernewek and it is these which make the dialect of Cornwall different from the dialects of South West England. Many of these words have cognates in Breton and Welsh.

Dialect	Kernewek	Breton	Welsh	English
bannel	banadhel	banazl	banadl	broom plant
broze	bros	brout	brwd	great heat
bullys	bili	bili	-	pebbles
carn	karn	karn	carn	rock-pile
crum	kromm	kroumm	crwm	crooked
growan	growan	grouan	graean	granite
kibble	kibell	kibell	-	tub
mabyer	mabyar	mab iar	mab iâr	pullet
tidden	tynn	tenn	tyn	tight, tender

3. The Three Great Industries of Cornwall

Fishing, farming and mining are three industries which stand out as being particularly Cornish. Cornwall has a huge length of coastline which includes many small coves from which our fishermen caught pilchards, mackerel and many other species of fish. It should come as no surprise to find many words of Kernewek origin that survived in the vocabulary in the fishing communities of our coast.

Cornish dialect	English meaning	Kernewek
agarrever, ajyreever	pollack	aswarudher
caboulen, caboleen	splashing stone	kabolenn
canker, cancer	crab	kanker
cock-an-bawba	toy boat	kokynn baban
crogan, croggan	shell	krogen
drethan	sandy patch	trethenn
froze, froase	tidal race	fros
morgy, mergy, murgy	dog fish	morgi
trestrem, tristram	bait	treustrumm
wrah, wraugh, wrath	wrasse	gwragh

Farming like fishing was a very important industry with an ancient history that ran through all Kernewek speaking periods of history. Some of the surviving Kernewek words are as follows.

Cornish Dialect	English Meaning	Kernewek
bougie, bowjey	cattle-shed	bowji
cack	filth, excrement	kawgh
crow, craw, crou	hut, sty	krow
crinion	barley bran	krinyon
durgy, dugy, dourgy	low turf hedge	dorge
fair mo, fair a mo	pig fair	fer mogh
mabyer, mabyers	pullets	mabyer
pedrack-mow	square mow	pedrek
scaw, scow, scoaw	elder trees	skaw
tyscan, tiskan	sheaf	tyskenn

Mining has always been associated with Cornwall. Tin was traded in pre-Roman times and copper, china clay, slate, granite, arsenic, silver and even uranium have been mined here. Cornwall is the greatest mining nation in the world and although the heyday of copper and tin production occurred after the language had died, miners still carried many words of Kernewek into the Cornish dialect.

Cornish dialect	English meaning	Kernewek
bal	a mine, digging	bal
cann, kand, cam	fluorspar	kann
coffin, coffen	surface diggings	koghynn
colpas	fulcrum	kolpes
costean	exploratory excavation	kostenn
growan	granite	growan
gunnies	worked out load	gonis
pulrose, polrose	wheel pit	pollros
scorran	branch of a lode	skorrenn
sigger, zyghyr, zighyr	to leak, ooze	syger

4. The Variation in Spelling of Cornish Dialect

As can be seen from the last three tables there is often more than one way to spell a dialect word. Sometimes this is due to the differences between East Cornwall and West

Cornwall. These variations have arisen due to West Cornwall retaining Kernewek until a later date than their fellow countrymen in the East. John Norden (c. 1548-1625) in his 'Description of Cornwall', written between 1597 and 1604, states;

> "...from Truro eastward it is in manner wholly English In the west part of the country, as in the Hundreds of Penwith and Kerrier, the Cornish tongue is most in use among the inhabitants..."

So Cornish was spoken widely west of Truro. One century later the great Celtic scholar Edward Lhuyd came to Cornwall. In a letter to a Mr. Rowland, Lhuyd says of Kernewek;

> "From five or six villages towards the Land's End, in which the The Cornish tongue was spoken in 1701, we must now descend to individuals, and from them trace it to its grave."

Kernewek was so weakened by 1700 that there were hardly two speakers of Kernewek living close enough to communicate[1]. The 1600s were a catastrophe for the language. During this time the majority of the population of West Cornwall gave up Kernewek and 'learned' the standard English of the day. Meanwhile the dialect of the Cornish people East of Truro had further developed in line with the dialects of South West England. Some differences are listed below.

East Cornish dialect	West Cornish dialect	English meaning	Kernewek
vardle	fardle	burden, package	fardell
viddy	fitty	proper, right	fyttya
zilver	silver	silver	arghans
vitt	feet	feet	dewdroes
emmit	muryan	ant	moryonenn

---

[1] There is conflicting evidence on this point. Although Dolly Pentreath was observed to converse, when aged, with two other elderly women, other accounts say that she spoke a mixture of Cornish and a strong English dialect.

Here the /f/ and /s/ of Western Cornish dialect i.e. the sounds of standard English of 1700 have not been softened by centuries of development to the /v/ and /z/ of the East Cornwall dialect. The last example illustrates that the Kernewek survivals are by and large found west of Truro. However as stated above the dialects were to some extent mingled by the movement of miners in the late 1800s, so much so that W. Fred Jago in his 'Glossary of the Cornish Dialect', published in 1882 says;

> For the sake of simplicity and uniformity, the writer has made this attempt to compile *one* glossary for the whole county [sic]."

Another factor which eroded the differences between East and West Cornwall dialect was the rise of Standard English i.e. Cornish dialect started to decline in use over all parts of the country.

5. The Decline of Dialect.

As there were no monoglot speakers of Kernewek by 1700, the language had virtually died. Thus the Standard English of this period was 'learned' by the inhabitants of West Cornwall. The English Church would have had little effect on the vernacular of the population. Thus all of Cornwall enjoyed maybe a century or two of linguistic stability. However the dialect of Cornwall has long been declining. In 1846, 'Specimens of the Cornish Provincial Dialect' talks of this decline.

> "The first part of this little collection contains specimens of the present Cornish provincial dialect, which is but little known out of the county [sic]; and even there is gradually wearing away in the towns; and is scarcely to be heard in its full richness except in the mining districts, or in the parts most remote from from traffic and intercourse with strangers."

Miss Margaret Courtney of Penzance, writing in 1880, says much the same.

> "With the introduction of the railways and the increased means of communication that has brought and brings every year more strangers to West Cornwall, the peculiar dialect is fast dying out..."

The reason for the start of the decline of dialect is given by Ben Batten in his book 'Old Newlyn Speech' (1984).

> "Only after the World War I did economic, social and other changes rapidly influence the way people spoke."

The upheaval of men leaving to fight in foreign parts and mixing with non-dialect speakers must have been detrimental to the Cornish dialect. The results are stated by Ben Batten.

> "Even before I entered college in 1930 many of the older words and expressions found in this book [Old Newlyn Speech] had begun to drop out of general use as more and more people, especially the young, became self-conscious of their vocabulary."

The next great change to effect dialect must have been the mass acquisition of the radio. Here a pure form of Standard English, BBC English no less, found its way into many Cornish homes on a regular basis. W.F. Ivey in 'A Dictionary of Cornish Dialect Words', 1976, proclaims that the dialect is to all intents and purposes dead but just retrievable from the older people.

> "It [his book] is, however, an attempt to record, as far as the limits of pronunciation will permit - a dialect used in former times in the more remote and isolated areas of SW Cornwall, as spoken and understood by the older inhabitants."

The curious phrase 'as spoken and understood' hints that some of these older inhabitants use dialect while others merely understand the dialect of Helston.

6. The Poor Image of Dialect Speakers

The cinema with its Hollywood films and wartime newsreels might have been the beginning of the poor image of dialect speakers. Advancement in the armed services may well have been barred to those who spoke a dialect which linked them to a region of Britain far from the political centre. Concern at the treatment of dialect speakers has been shown for a long time. Mr. W. M. Symonds in 'Old Cornwall', the magazine of the Federation of Old Cornwall Societies, back in 1936, expresses his concern about dialect readings performed at Old Cornwall Society meetings;

> "To raise laughs, at least one of the characters is a simpleton, and it is he or she who usually talks the broadest Cornish. Surely this is not the way to gain respect for our dialect."

When we laugh at Jethro's Denzil Penberthy character or the Mock Mayor of Penzance on Mazy Day we are in fact strengthening the English stereotypes of Cornish people. Ben Batten attacks the main stream image makers.

> "All fisherfolk and rustics of our South-West definitely do not, and did not, show characteristics of slow speech and slow wits; that tiresome and stock idea has been propagated from patronising and ignorant dramatists and writers of fiction from elsewhere."

The dialect of Cornwall is something precious for a number of reasons and we should respect it at least for the sake of politeness to the people who speak it. Today's Cornish patriot is a very complicated animal. I have heard children in school flip from Standard English to the broadest of Cornish dialect and back again. These days many people are learning Kernewek and a small number of people can express themselves in all three ways according to whom they are conversing with - definitely not Oo ar, Oo ar!

7.1 The Overlap Between the Cornish Dialect and Kernewek

This overall overlap is very slight indeed. Having lived in Troon, Liskeard and Grampound Road, learnt Kernewek in Camborne, Liskeard and London and then taught Kernewek at Pengegeon, Camborne, Grampound Road and St. Austell I have noted the overlap to be virtually non-existent. Using Cornish dialect as a gateway to Kernewek is not possible. Many beginners don't come from Cornwall let alone the Western counties of Penwith and Kerrier where the greatest number of Kernewek survivals are to be found. Dialect is used predominantly by older people but Kernewek attracts people of all ages. The farming, fishing and mining industries sadly employ less and less people and have become mechanized and modernized. It was within these professions that the Cornish dialect was at its full strength.

7.2 Grammar

Many people have stated that there is some link between the grammar of Cornish dialect and Kernewek. Dialect experts usually give glossaries and omit to mention grammar. So to assess the Dialect/Kernewek overlap in term of grammar is virtually impossible. However the grammar of Kernewek is very different from standard English and the majority of Cornish dialect grammar is derived from English so the overlap is minimal. Even the most quoted example; 'my a wra gul henna', literally 'I do do that' is not all that it seems. This construction was over promoted by Nance in an attempt to link Kernewek and the Cornish dialect, as pointed out by Julyan Holmes in his paper 'Nebes Geryow Moy A-dro dhe Gernewek' - some comments on Dr. N.J.A. Williams' 'Cornish Today'.

7.3 Spelling

The spelling of Cornish dialect can give us important clues to the true sounds contained in the words. But to base the spelling of Kernewek on that of dialect produces three main problems:

a) which form of dialect spelling is the most correct e.g. *brail, brails, breal, bree'al, breeal, brellal* and *bridga* all for the word 'brithel' (mackerel),

b) How are sounds not found in Cornish dialect or standard English to be written?

c) The huge body of written Kernewek gives us a far greater insight into spelling and pronunciation than the dialect ever can.

The variation in spelling even between places in the same geographical area is shown by the mackerel chants collected by Robert Morton Nance about 1914 from the fishing coves of County Penwith.

1) Porthleven, 1914 - Brail; and his mate; druja; peswarra; timpes; withes; all scraw! all along the line - o!

2) Mousehole, 1868 - Bree'al; a's meeut; truja; peswartha; pempes; wethes; all scrawl! all along the line - o, boys!

3) Mousehole, 1914 - Brail; mata; drooja; beswartha; pempes; withes; white scrawed!

4) Newlyn, 1875 - Breal; meeat; truja, beswartha; pempes, wethes; all ascrowed all along the line - oh!

5) Newlyn, 1883 - Breal; meta; triya; peswartha; pempthez; whethez; all in crawed.

6) Newlyn, 1888 - Brails; mate; dridgey; pempes; witheys; als crowd, all along the line oh!

7) St. Ives, 1914 - Brail; a mata; tempa; didga; peswilla; all along the line -o, a - waatin' outside all like to a weddin', scrowl - o!

8) St. Ives, 1914 - Bridga; menta; didga; tempa; scrowla, all along the line - o!

9) St. Ives, 1914 - Brella, mata, didga, pumpa, all scrowl, line - o!

10) Mounts Bay, 1940 - Mackerel! Braal; rudgal; pescwara; pempes; wethes; all scrawl, all along the line O!

In Kernewek the chant would be ; Brithel; mata, tressa, peswara, pympes, hweghves; warbarth oll a-hys an linenn - o!

The orthography of Cornish dialect, and that used in spelling Cornish place names, is derived from English and can not be used for a different language. If I were to propose that the French language should be written in English orthography e.g. 'an, duh, twa, catra, sank, seese, set, weet, nuff, deese.' I would be rightly ridiculed. So why should Kernewek be written as if it were some off-shoot of English which it clearly is not.

The vocabulary of Kernewek is drawn from a number of sources. Because Kernewek is a revived language all sources are needed to provide a vocabulary fit for a living language of today.

1) Old Kernewek (the written Kernewek of 800-1200)
2) Middle Kernewek (the written Kernewek of 1200-1575)
3) Late Kernewek (the written Kernewek of 1575-1800)
4) Place-names in Kernewek
5) Family names in Kernewek
6) Breton and Welsh cognates
7) English and French loan words
8) Self-generated neologisms
9) and the Cornish dialect.

It must be stated that the bulk of vocabulary, grammar and idiom is borrowed from the Middle Cornish period. This is so because some 84% of literature written in Kernewek comes from this period.

8.1 The Place of Cornish Dialect in Kernewek

8.2 Vocabulary

Cornish dialect has played an important role in providing Kernewek speakers with new words. Just as important is the role of supporting the use of many words found only in one other source e.g. the word 'moryon' (ants) is found only in Late Kernewek but is also found in Cornish dialect as 'muryan' and 'kibell' is found as a Breton cognate 'kibell' (a tub) but also in the Cornish dialect as 'kibble'

8.3 Intonation

This is the lovely sing song way in which a stream of words is delivered by broad dialect speakers of West Cornwall. Personally I'm not sure if this can be taught like grammar and vocabulary but if an individual can speak Kernewek with this intonation then they certainly should. Very little academic study has been done on this but when speaking Kernewek or Cornish dialect it just sounds 'fitty.'

8.4 Sounds

Since Kernewek and English are different languages and Cornish dialect is no more than a deviant form of the English language, the overlap in phonology is slight indeed. However, there are two sounds which exist in both dialect and Kernewek which do not exit in standard English. These are the long <e> sound [ɛ:] and the dialectectal realization of <ow> sound, the <ew> sound in Kernewek [ɛw].

The long [ɛ:] sound in dialect 'lane', 'gate' and 'trade' is roughly equivalent to the sound in the Kernewek words 'men' (stone), 'mel' (honey) and 'den' (man).

The diphthong [ɛw] is found in Welsh, Breton and Cornish dialect but it is not found in Standard English. The word 'cow' is pronounced [kaw] in standard English but is pronounced [kɛw] in dialect. In Kernewek classes I have found that all Cornish people, both East and West, have no difficulties with this 'new' sound. The phrase 'how now brown cow' displays whether the person was brought up in Cornwall or England very clearly indeed. This built in advantage of the dialect speaker is counteracted by the difficulty in pronouncing the diphthong

<aw>. This sound is less common in Kernewek but is found in 'maw' (boy) and 'naw' (nine). This should be pronounced as in the [ow] as in standard English 'how'. Some speakers of Kernewek, myself included, often let the [aw] sound slip to the [ɛw] sound. This is bad practice because the two sounds are obviously distinct in Kernewek. This is shown by the existence of pairs of words such as 'new' (sink) and 'naw' (nine) and 'glew' (translucent, penetrating) and 'glaw' (rain). But since <ew> is more common in Kernewek than <aw> to be a dialect speaker is an advantage.

9 Wit and Wisdom

Probably the greatest contribution to be made to Kernewek by the Cornish dialect is the wealth of phrases that reflect the wisdom and humour of our forefathers. Compare the two sentences below and see how the use of a dialect phrase makes the Kernewek (and the English) more Cornish!

1) **Pur dewl o, mar dewl ma na yllys gweles dha dhorn a-rag dha vejeth**

It was very dark, so dark one could not see your hand in front of your face

2) **Pur dewl o, mar dewl avel sagh kroust an jowl**

It was very dark, as dark as the devil's crowst bag

Rod Lyon at the Pennseythun Gernewek '95 (Cornish Language Weekend), held at Maenporth, gave a talk on doing just this. We should all heed his plea and remember the dialect of our up-bringing or if unlucky enough to be raised East of the Tamar then consult the many books on Cornish dialect and add colour and life to our spoken Kernewek.

Here is a small selection of dialect phrases that no speaker of Kernewek should be without:

Mar vedhow avel gravath ros	*drunk as a hand cart* - the path of a heavily loaded wheel barrow being similar to that of a drunken man
Mar yeyn avel kwilkyn	*as cold as a quilkin* - quilkin is a Kernewek survival and means frog
Moy bejethow ages klokk an dre Gammbronn	*more faces than Camborne town clock* - said of a two faced person
Mar ger avel safron	*as dear as saffron* - the most expensive spice in the world but used in traditional Cornish cuisine - perhaps due to smuggling
Ow mos avel ki hir	*goin' like a long dog* - a long dog being a greyhound
Fyttys avel monger	*fit like a mongern* - a horse collar, mong is Kernewek for a mane
Mar leven avel bulhorn	*as smooth as a bullhorn* - a snail
Kepar ha band Trerigni, tri skat dhe lergh	*like Tregoney band, three scats behind* - here a scat is a musical beat
Mar dhown avel Dorkoth	*as deep as Dolcoath* - the deepest mine in Cornwall
Hwoffys kepar ha kwilkyn	*blawd* (blown) *up like a wilkie* (a frog)- someone full of themselves

Many expressions use the names of local characters which gained notoriety but now have been lost in the mists of time. These still can be translated and build a link between the Kernewek of today and the Cornish dialect of yesteryear.

Pasti mar hir avel krowd Yowann Bodella	a pasty as long as Jan Bodella's fiddle
Skethennek kepar ha Jy ha'y grys yn-mes	ragged like Jy with his shirt hanging out
Kepar ha Wella orth an maler	like Billy o' the grinder - someone who works too hard and shows up everybody else
Kepar ha heyji Tiek Hoskin, moy kows ages kolon	like Farmer Hoskin's ducks, more gab than guts - over noisy

10. Conclusion

The Cornish dialect is different from dialects of English because of the influence of Kernewek. It is this influence that Kernewek speakers and academics should tease out and use to make a bridge between the English speaking and Kernewek speaking communities of Cornwall.

11. Bibliography

1. A Glossary of the Cornish Dialect by K.C. Philips, 1993, Tabb House, Lannwedhenek/Padstow, Kernow/Cornwall.

2. A Dictionary of Cornish Dialect Words by W.F. Ivey, 1976 Helston Printers, Hellys/Helston, Kernow/Cornwall.

3. A Glossary of Cornish Sea Words by R.M. Nance, 1963 The Federation of Old Cornwall Societies, Kernow/Cornwall.

4. A Cornish Hotchpotch by Kathleen Hawke, 1989 Dyllansow Truran, Rysrudh/Redruth, Kernow/Cornwall.

5. Cornish Sayings, Superstitions and Remedies by Kathleen Hawke 1975 Dyllansow Truan, Rysrudh/Redruth, Kernow/ Cornwall.

6. Specimens of Cornish Provincial Dialect by Uncle Jan Trenoodle, 1846, John Russel Smith, Loundres/London, Pow Sows/England.

7. Glossary of Words in Use in Cornwall, 1880 West Cornwall - Miss M.A. Courtney, East Cornwall - Thomas Q. Couch The English Dialect Society, Pow Sows/England.

8. Old Newlyn Speech by Ben Batten, 1984 Newlyn Printers, Lulynn/Newlyn, Kernow/Cornwall.

9. Glossary of Cornish Provincial Words by F. Jago,1882

10. A Glossary of Celtic Words in Cornish Dialect by R.M. Nance, 1921 Royal Cornwall Polytechnic, Aberfal/Falmouth, Kernow/Cornwall.

11. Unpublished list of St. Neot Dialect Words by Alan Pascoe, 1927 Menydh/Mount, Kernow/Cornwall.

12. Gerlyver Kernewek Kemmyn by Dr. Ken George, 1993 Kesva an Taves Kernewek/Cornish Language Board, Kernow/Cornwall.

13. A Grammar of Modern Cornish by Wella Brown, 1993 Kesva an Taves Kernewek/Cornish Language Board, Kernow/Cornwall.

14. The Death of Cornish by P.A.S. Pool, 1982 Kesva an Taves Kernewek/Cornish Language Board, Kernow/Cornwall.

15. Old Cornwall - Federation of Old Cornwall Socities, Kernow/Cornwall.

16. Language and History of Cornwall by Martyn Wakelin, 1972 Leeds Dialect Survey, Leeds, Pow Sows/England.

Other titles in this series are:

A background to Cornish, number one:
Place-names in Cornwall
by Ken George, Pol Hodge, Julyan Holmes & Graham Sandercock.

A background to Cornish, number two:
The formation of Cornish place-names
by Wella Brown and Graham Sandercock.

A background to Cornish, number three:
A very brief history of the Cornish language
by Graham Sandercock.

All available from:

Kesva an Taves Kernewek
(The Cornish Language Board)
65 Churchtown
Gwinear
Hayle
Cornwall
☎ and fax 01736 850878

Send for a full list of publications.